Little Windjammer

Little Windjammer

by Harriet Kenney

photographs by Isabel Gordon

E. P. Dutton & Co., Inc.   New York

FIRST EDITION

Text Copyright © 1969 by Harriet Kenney. Photographs Copyright © 1969
by Isabel Gordon.
Published simultaneously in Canada by
Clarke, Irwin & Company Limited, Toronto and Vancouver

Library of Congress Catalog Card Number: 72-81711

To Erin, Tegan and Peter

Some families adopt round plump babies.
Some adopt stray wet kittens,
Or sad-eyed black and white puppies.

Our family adopted a boat.
An abandoned, unloved, uncared-for boat.

First we were dreaming about a boat.
Then we were wishing for a boat . . . a boat.
And next, we were *looking* for a boat!

The last patches of winter snow had melted away.
Spring things were happening all around.
The sailing season was soon to begin and
Our search for a boat continued.
We had just given up hope when—

Discovery!

In a gigantic nest of weeds and sea grass
At the far end of an old boatyard,
There she was,
Alone,
Except for one friend, a seagull,
Muttering thoughts in deep throaty tones.
Mr. Barnes, the boatyard man, called her
A gaff-rigged sloop.

"Built these boats 'round Gloucester
More th'n fifty years ago.
Sailed here off the New England coast,
Crew catchin' enough fish to feed a village.
Faced nor'easters when other boats
Set tight to anchor.
Powerful-engined boats
Do the work nowadays.
Nobody needs her anymore."

"Does she float?"

"Who can tell?
Hull needs caulkin', scraping and paint.
Hasn't been in the water for years.
Who can tell?"

"Does she have sails?"

"Yep, canvas is old, has a rip or two . . .
And there's a mast stored in the shed."

Friend seagull pushed strong legs
Against her deck, and flapping his great wings,
Headed out to sea
Seeking some new adventure.

Could we? *Could we?*
She needs a family.
Could we take her home?

Mother and father stepped aside.
They were having a private conversation.

And then we heard father say,
"Will you haul her for us?
We'd like to adopt
This poor little windjammer!"

By Saturday,
This new member of our family
Was settled down beneath the trees
In our yard.

She belongs to *us!*

Let's explore!
Get a stool, no,
Get a tall ladder!

Hello! wonderful old sad-looking boat.
It's Spring!
We're your new family.

Suddenly
The old boat trembled
With legs scrambling over and down,
Heads poking in and out,
Hands reaching, touching, exploring,
Voices shouting
With each new discovery.

An anchor!
Tons of rope!
Look at the cabin.
Careful, it's dark down there, Peter.
A little stove–
That's a galley stove.
Bunks!
We can have overnights.
A map.
That's a chart, silly.
A cup–

A horn!
WHOOOooomMM
It's a foghorn
WHROOOOooomMMMMNnn
Attention, all ships at sea!
Hail! the launching of the new queen!

She doesn't look very happy to me
How can you call her a queen?
I love her,
But will she ever sail?

Remember what Mr. Barnes said,
Father, too–
"Needs caulking, scraping and paint."

What's caulking?

Fill the cracks
Fill the cracks

We need caulking
Packs and packs

Fill the cracks
Fill the cracks

And scrunching, scratching sounds
Told of work going on in the woods.

Such faded old paint,
How many colors buried underneath?
Whoops! No paint puddles, I promised.
This is fun,
Spreading yellow sunshine
Through the cabin.

A warm hideaway from those big storms
Mr. Barnes talked about.
It'll be cozy down here nighttimes.

You are quite a sight, dear old sloop,
With your funny looking patches.
Many Saturdays of scrubbing, scraping and sanding,
Some with tears and sore elbows, but
Now you are ready for your
Shiny coat of paint.

Scat little inch-worm,
Wiggling your tail in my nice blue paint.
We must hurry—it's almost time for
Our trip to the ocean.

One last daub of blue.
I hope it dries before the
Boathauler gets here.
Oh! Boat, you look so pretty!
I hope your patches hold.
Are all your cracks fixed?
Will you float?

The boathauler is coming . . .
He's coming today.
I hope she won't sink.

A rumble is heard.
It's the truck. The boathauler
Backs a long, flat trailer down
Into the woods. Bit by bit,
The men roll our boat
Onto the trailer.
Boat and cradle must balance perfectly.
"Steady now," they call,
"Ready, pull."

She moves out of the woods
Like a big black bird
And starts on her way to the harbor.

Let's follow!

Go faster, Father
She may need help.

"No, she's fine now. The highway's smooth
And she balances well."

Do you think she's really ready?

"There's the harbor,
We'll soon find out."

The boatmen get ready to launch.

"Release the trailer."
"Steady now–" they call
"Down she goes."

Splash!

She's tipping!

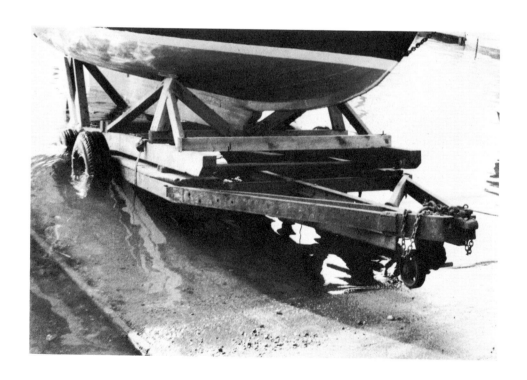

"No–
She's settling in."

She's staying up,
She's not going to sink.

Father guides her to the dock.
"All's well–seams are holding!
Good work, little ones."

"Now for the job of setting the mast."

The harbor crane stands ready for father's signal.
"Better use double line, she's heavy.
Okay, take her up now."

"Stand back!"

The giant mast swings awkwardly above
her deck.

Mr. Barnes didn't tell us—it's huge!
It's tall as a tree.
It looks like a flagpole!
Yes, and when the sails wave . . .
Crack!
A rope snaps.
She's falling!
Father leaps for the broken line,
And then with the help of the crane
Manages to step the mast into place.

Wheeuwww! That was close!

A great puzzle of pulleys, line, and rigging
Litter the decks.
"Come aboard, crew,
I need many hands to unfold and fasten.
Mother, the old canvas sail needs a stitch or two!"

Hold still, boat,
We're dressing you in your sailing clothes
As fast as we can.

When can we pull up her sails?

Have patience!
She's ready, but are *we?*

We must chart our course,
Listen to forecasts,
Check the tides,
Pack and plan.
Be patient.

Where are the life jackets?
Where are the charts?

Get a lantern
Books
Food
Don't forget first aid
And the fire extinguisher.

Make a list.
    Compass
    Lines
    Sweaters
    Sleeping bags
    Flashlights
    Bubble gum
    Games

It's like waiting for your birthday.
Each new day brings you closer and closer
Until you feel you'll pop before it comes.
Then one morning, you open your eyes

And you know
It's here!

The call of a gull echoes across the harbor.
Tiny boats nod a good morning.

"All aboard!
Check the lines
All right, cast off."

The chug of our small engine
Is the only sound in the sleepy river.
Morning mist wets the deck.
"It's slippery–hold tight, Peter
Watch for the channel markings, everyone."

A fog horn blows from far out at sea.
She seems to know her way.
Could I hold the tiller?

When can we put up the sails?

"After we go under the bridges
And come to open water."

A call has been made to open the town bridge.

All traffic stops
The bridgemen turn a giant wheel round and round.
The bridge swings open for *us*.

"Thank you,"
We call.

Our black sailing bird is
Almost ready to fly.
One more bridge–the railroad bridge.
"Signal the tower!"
Blow the horn . . . blow.

We watch the giant tracks lift skyward.

Under we go.

Just beyond the point
Our bow bites into crisp, choppy waves.
The sun warms the deck.

A breeze whispers high in the rigging.
We've left the river behind.
Now can we hoist the sails?

"All right, crew,
Turn off the motor.
Mother, head her up into the wind."

Father tugs the halyard
And the heavy sail
Climbs the mast
With a thunderous
Flapping, clapping sound.

The sail takes command!

The boat leaps forward into the waves.
She begins to really fly.

We all laugh—our little windjammer,
Such a show-off on her first sail!

Is it a dream?
A wonderful, impossible dream?
No!

A wave spanks her bow
Salty spray wets our hair
People wave from other boats and admire.
We feel so proud.

A seagull races our Little Windjammer
As she wings across the water.

Join us, Mr. Gull!
Don't look so puzzled–
Of course, she's your old boatyard friend.
No more snoozing away the years
In her landlocked nest.

Look at her go!
There are seas to conquer,
Islands to explore–
Maybe she even remembers some buried treasure . . .

Come along!

Nautical Glossary

Boatyard: a land area, near the water, where boats are built, repaired, and stored

Bow: the most forward part of a boat

Bunk: the place a person sleeps aboard a boat

Cabin: an enclosed living area aboard a boat

Canvas: a boating word for sail material

Cast off: to let go of the line holding the boat to the dock

Caulking: a soft putty used to fill the cracks in the boat planking

Channel markings: big red and black floats to mark the deep water of river or harbor

Chart: a map of the sea

Compass: an instrument for telling directions

Cradle: a wooden support to hold a boat when hauled out of water

Crew: a group of helpers aboard a boat

Fog horn: a horn blown as a warning during fog at sea, or to call attention to another boat

Gaff-rigged: a mainsail that is raised and supported by a short boom

62

Galley: the kitchen area of a boat

Halyard: a line used for raising sails (or flags)

Hull: the outer planking of a boat

Launch: to slide the boat into the water

Line: a boating name for rope

Mast: the upright pole that supports rigging and sails

Rigging: lines, wires, and pulleys used to support the mast and control the sails

Sloop: a one-masted sail boat

Tiller: a lever used to steer a boat

Windjammer: a nickname for oldtime sailing vessels

Harriet Kenney graduated from Southern Connecticut College and taught first grade in the Westport, Connecticut, schools for five years. Then for two years she was a full-time school art instructor. While teaching she sometimes developed her own story units and discovered how much she enjoyed writing. Now she is married to Peter Kenney, has three children, lives in Westport, and still finds time to paint. *Little Windjammer* is her first book. Although she and her husband have crewed on all size boats for years, they never owned one until they bought this gaff-rigged sloop. The boat is about fifty years old, thirty feet long, and sturdy enough for the Kenney children.

Isabel Gordon grew up in Chicago and attended Northwestern University School of Journalism. Before her marriage she was a copywriter in Chicago and New York. Her husband bought her a camera so she could take pictures of his boat. She never took *those* pictures but she became an accomplished photographer and has illustrated three other children's books, *The ABC Hunt* with her own text, *The Shadow Book* written by Beatrice de Regniers, and *I Talk to Elephants* written by Myra Cohen Livingston. She loves photography but feels it is appropriate for children's books only in very special cases. Luckily, she considers *Little Windjammer* one of those cases. The Gordons live in Green's Farms, Connecticut, and have a teen-age son, Richard.